Ronta

The Lucky Donkey

Story and art by Shiro Fujimoto

Pauline
BOOKS & MEDIA

Many,
  many years ago,
    very near a town
      called Nazareth,
    there was a farm.

On this farm
  there lived
    lots of animals.

A little donkey lived there, too.

His name was Ronta.

He was not especially clever.

He was not especially quick.

But

he was kind

and very gentle.

"Ha ha! Look at you! Slow as a snail!"
the other animals laughed at Ronta.

They called him names,
and wouldn't let him play
with them.

Ronta felt very sad,
because he thought
he didn't have
any friends.

But every evening,
   his mother
      told him
his favourite story.

It was a wonderful story about
   a very important person.

   "It is said that one day soon
   a Saviour will come,"
his mother told him.

"He will want
to be with
the children,
with the poor,
the simple.

"He will be
able to see
what is
in our hearts."

"Would he like me?"
wondered Ronta.

"Oh,
how I wish
I could meet him!"

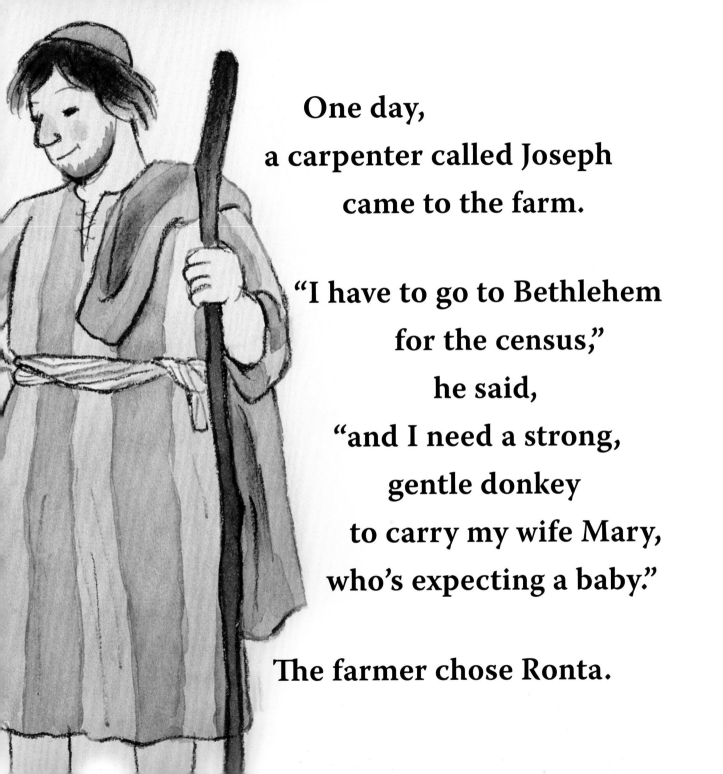

One day,
a carpenter called Joseph
came to the farm.

"I have to go to Bethlehem
for the census,"
he said,
"and I need a strong,
gentle donkey
to carry my wife Mary,
who's expecting a baby."

The farmer chose Ronta.

And so Ronta left home.

"Goodbye,
    my little Ronta,"
        said his mother.

"Goodbye, Ronta,"
called the animals,
who were now sorry to see him go.

The path
from Nazareth
to Bethlehem
winds up
and
down
over tall hills
and
deep valleys.

Ronta liked to listen as Mary and Joseph talked about the baby Mary was expecting.

During the nights
it was lonely under the stars.

Sometimes a wolf howled.

How tiny and afraid Ronta felt!

But then
    he remembered the Saviour
    and was no longer
    afraid.

While Joseph rested
and Mary slept,
Ronta kept guard
all through
the night.

Just as Ronta cared
        for Joseph and Mary,
                they in turn
                        cared for him.

As they approached Bethlehem
they still talked about the baby,
but
to the little donkey's surprise
they now often
talked about
the Saviour as well.

Ronta began to wonder.

At last
they arrived in
Bethlehem.
Mary and Joseph
wanted a room
for the night,
but nobody
had one to spare.

"Sorry,
we're all full up.
But there's
a stable
down the road."

That night,
Ronta waited patiently
outside the stable.

Soon
his question
would be answered.

Was Mary's baby
the Saviour
that was to come?

And then the stable filled with light.

All of a sudden
the sky
was full of angels
shouting for joy.

"Glory to God
in the highest
and
peace to his people
on earth!"

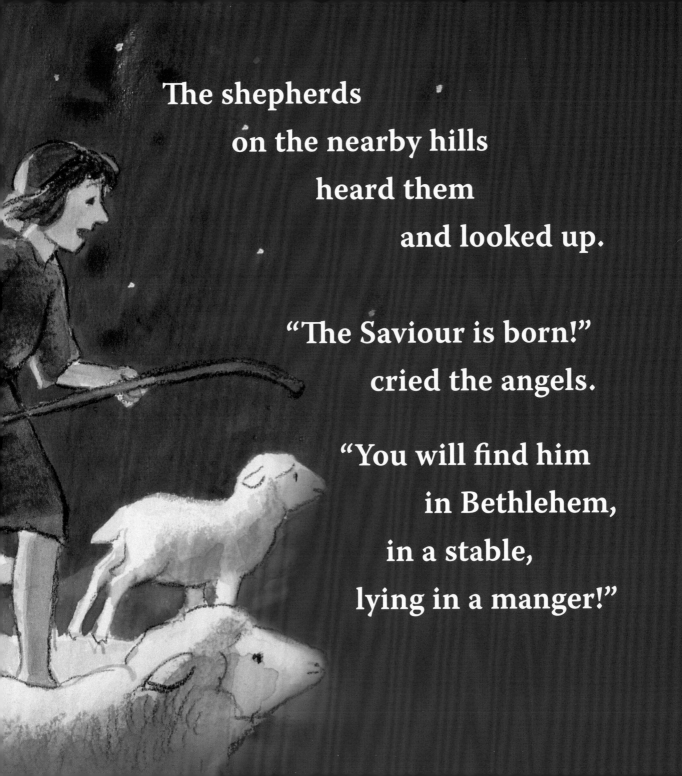

The shepherds
on the nearby hills
heard them
and looked up.

"The Saviour is born!"
cried the angels.

"You will find him
in Bethlehem,
in a stable,
lying in a manger!"

"Then it's true!

Mary's little baby is the Saviour!"

"Jesus, you are the Saviour

my mother told me about!"

"Oh, how I do wish my friends were here now

to meet you too ...!"

Full of joy,

Ronta went back.

"The Saviour is born, my friends.

I carried his mother Mary!"

The animals
wanted to see Jesus, too.
Together with Ronta
and the shepherds they stood,
filled with
amazement.

Ronta's friends
were so proud of him now.

"You are the luckiest donkey
in the world."

And he was
the luckiest donkey in the world.

He, Ronta, the slow one,
had been chosen to see
the coming of the Saviour.

Original story and art
Shiro Fujimoto
© Daughters of St Paul, Tokuo 1984

First produced as a slide presentation
© St Paul Audio Visual Productions, UK, 1985

Translated by Margaret Brauer

First published in the United Kingdom in 2010 by Pauline Books & Media, Slough SL3 6BS
© 2010 Pauline Books & Media UK

Cover/book design MaryLouise Winters fsp

ISBN 9781904785484

Pauline
BOOKS & MEDIA
Middle Green, Slough SL3 6BS – UK
0044 (0) 1753 577629
www.PaulineUK.org
email: marketing@pauline-uk.org

Pauline Books & Media is an expression of the ministry of the Daughters of St Paul,
a group of religious sisters whose ministry is to proclaim the Good News of Jesus Christ using the means of communication.